Fire protection

your responsibilities under the Fire Safety Order (RRFSO)

GW00569396

BMTRADA

ISBN: 978-1-909594-22-7
First edition published in 2014 by BM TRADA

This is a technical book for business managers. While every effort is made to ensure the accuracy of the advice given, the company cannot accept liability for loss or damage arising from the information supplied. Owing to its complexity, legal advice may be needed to define responsibilities and duties under the RRFSO

BMTRADA

BM TRADA provides independent certification, testing, inspection, training, technical services and information to the timber, building, fire and furniture industries. It is also the appointed service provider for TRADA's and FIRA's research, information and membership administration

The BM TRADA bookshop offers a wide range of technical publications for professionals: http://bookshop.bmtrada.com

Prepared by Peter Barker, BM TRADA's Senior Consultant – Fire, with Matt Thompson Communications and the BM TRADA publishing team. Thanks to Nicholas Coombe of London Fire Brigade

Cover photograph: © iStockphoto.com/olaser

All photographs and illustrations are © BM TRADA except those otherwise credited in the captions

BM TRADA
Chiltern House
Stocking Lane
Hughenden Valley
High Wycombe
Buckinghamshire HP14 4ND
tel: +44 (0)1494 569600
fax: +44 (0)1494 565487
email: publications@bmtradagroup.com
website: www.bmtradagroup.com

MIX
Paper from
responsible sources
FSC
www.fsc.org   FSC® C011748

'Getting started with' is a series of introductory-level guides including:

- CE marking for construction products
- Energy management and ISO 50001:2011 certification
- Chain of custody certification for forest products
- Chain of custody project certification
- Factory production control for construction product certification
- Sustainable palm oil certification (RSPO)

Visit the BM TRADA bookshop: http://bookshop.bmtrada.com

Fire protection
your responsibilities under the Fire Safety Order (RRFSO)

The Regulatory Reform (Fire Safety) Order imposes important duties and responsibilities for protection of people from fire in all premises other than private homes. The Fire Safety Order takes a broad view of responsibility and some may not realise they have legal responsibilities for fire protection.

This accessible guide to fire prevention will help you get to grips with the Fire Safety Order, your role as a 'responsible person' (or quasi-responsible person), how to implement the Order in your organisation and who can support you in this process.

Intended for duty holders including the employer and its directors, senior managers, property owners and occupiers in the public and private sectors, this book is also for those who influence decisions such as fire and rescue authorities and local authorities (the 'enforcing bodies') as well as fire inspectors, fire risk assessors and product manufacturers.

Contents

SECTION 1: THE BACKGROUND

1 Introduction

This book explains your duties to protect the safety of people from fire in existing buildings under the Regulatory Reform (Fire Safety) Order 2005 (RRFSO),[1] the chief piece of legislation in England and Wales regulating all premises other than private homes. It refers to the relevant articles in the RRFSO, for example, 'article 15'.

In Scotland, the equivalent pieces of legislation are the Fire (Scotland) Act 2005 and the Fire Safety (Scotland) Regulations 2006.[2] In Northern Ireland, they are Part 3 of the Fire and Rescue Services (Northern Ireland) Order 2006 and the Fire Safety Regulations (Northern Ireland) 2010.[3] All this legislation takes a similar approach to the RRFSO.

Who should read it?

Throughout the book, 'you' refers to the chief duty-holders, known as 'responsible persons', or to quasi-responsible persons (otherwise known as '5.3/5.4 persons' after the relevant article in the RRFSO). Generally speaking, the responsible person is the employer and its directors, senior managers, or the property owner or occupier of premises, in both the private and public sectors. Quasi-responsible persons can include a much wider range of people – facilities managers, managing agents, employees, engineers, contractors, supervisors, leaseholders, etc – provided they have sufficient control over the premises or parts thereof, even if only temporarily. See *Chapter 2* for more about responsible and quasi-responsible persons.

The book is also for people who can influence responsible persons, such as:

- fire and rescue authorities and local authorities – the 'enforcing bodies'
- fire inspectors
- fire risk assessors
- product manufacturers.

How is it structured?

The book comprises seven chapters in two sections. The first section is essential background information, including a whistle-stop tour of the

RRFSO's mechanics. The second section looks in more detail at what you should do in practice, structured to make sense to a business manager.

What does it cover?

The book highlights the important duties and responsibilities imposed on you by the RRFSO, and explains how third parties can help you to discharge those duties. Wherever useful, the book lists sources of further information. It touches briefly on some of the technical aspects of passive fire protection but is not intended as a technical guide. Equally, the scope does not look at the specific requirements for different types of premises. For this kind of information, the sectoral guides published by the Department for Communities and Local Government are an excellent starting point.

In England and Wales, the Government publishes a series of 16 free sectoral guides explaining the duties of responsible persons under the RRFSO,[4] listed as follows:

1. Making your premises safe from fire
2. Fire safety risk assessment: 5-step checklist
3. Fire safety risk assessment: means of escape for disabled people
4. Do you have paying guests?
5. Fire safety risk assessment: animal premises and stables
6. Fire safety risk assessment: open-air events and venues
7. Fire safety risk assessment: transport premises and facilities
8. Fire safety risk assessment: healthcare premises
9. Fire safety risk assessment: residential care premises
10. Fire safety risk assessment: theatres, cinemas and similar premises
11. Fire safety risk assessment: factories and warehouses
12. Fire safety risk assessment: large places of assembly
13. Fire safety risk assessment: small and medium places of assembly
14. Fire safety risk assessment: educational premises
15. Fire safety risk assessment: sleeping accommodation
16. Fire safety risk assessment: offices and shops.

Fire safety advice is also available in:

- Local Authorities Coordinators of Regulatory Services (LACoRS), *Housing – Fire Safety: Guidance on fire safety provisions for certain types of existing housing* (2008).[5]

- Local Government Association, *Fire safety in purpose-built blocks of flats* (2012).[6]
- The Health and Safety Executive, *Fire safety in construction, second edition* (2010).[7]

The RRFSO is working

Figure 1: Fire remains a threat to unprotected persons and property
Photo: London Fire Brigade

In Great Britain, government policies to protect the lives of people from fire are working, especially in premises covered by the RRFSO. For example, just 17 fatalities (or less than 5% of all deaths from fire) were recorded in such premises in Great Britain during 2012-13.[8] This is a rate of 0.25 people per million population. (To put this in context, there were 28 deaths on the road per million population in 2012,[9] making roads more than a hundred times more deadly.) The number of non-fatal casualties was just over 1,000.

Trends in fatalities, casualties and the numbers of fires have been declining for decades and continue to do so. Even so, in premises covered by the RRFSO there are still far too many fires – 19,900 of varying severity in 2012-13. Of these, a surprisingly large number – about 30% – were started deliberately. Even if people are extremely unlikely to be harmed by fire at work or in public buildings in Great Britain (thanks in part to the RRFSO), fires obviously have other very grave consequences and the ultimate objective must be to prevent them entirely.

Why is fire protection important?

Unfortunately, fire is always a threat and so premises must be protected. Fire protection is a bit like an insurance policy: the costs are irretrievable and the benefits only felt in the event that you suffer a fire, which might never happen. If it does, of course, you will be very glad you did protect yourself: people are much safer, the fire is much less damaging, and business returns to normal more quickly.

If you haven't carried out your legal responsibilities under the RRFSO with due diligence, the consequences of a fire are more likely to be catastrophic. Deaths and severe casualties among friends, colleagues and anyone else who happens to be present at the time are a very real possibility. Added to that are existential threats to your 'undertaking' – usually a business – and the probability of prosecution with attendant penalties of fines and jail terms.

So while having to consider fire risks is unwelcome amid all the other competing priorities in your life, the consequences of not doing so are so severe that you cannot afford to ignore them. It ceases to be primarily a legal duty and instead is one of common sense. The precautionary principle absolutely applies.

What do you need to know?

The way the RRFSO is framed puts the duty to be responsible for fire safety of their undertakings on ordinary non-specialists like you. This duty can be very onerous; it requires a broad understanding of many specialist technical subjects, all of them a field of expertise by themselves:

- **The legal position:** including your liabilities under the RRFSO and with your insurers
- **The management of fire safety:** including training, maintenance of measures, regular inspections, updating emergency plans, checking compliance
- **Fire risk assessment:** including knowing how to identify hazards and the best way to deal with them
- **How fires occur and spread:** including an understanding of the physics of ignition, the products of fire, and the fire resistance of different materials
- **Effects of fire on people and their behaviour:** including both physiological and psychological issues
- **Fire prevention:** including managerial, behavioural and technical aspects and how they should work together
- **Passive fire protection:** including how to optimize engineered solutions that take account of how buildings work

- **Active fire protection:** including a complexity in understanding how to fight different kinds of fire and the best methods for achieving that
- **Means of escape:** including the most effective ways to evacuate people safely from buildings and account for them.

How can you comply?

How you fulfil your duty is mostly a matter of choice. In small premises with few people, no unusual hazards and excellent escape routes to places of safety, compliance is generally straightforward and inexpensive. However, the more complex the premises, the more people you have to consider, and the more hazardous the operations and substances, the harder it gets.

Published guides, training courses, and other information resources can help you to understand all aspects, including the physics of fire and how people react in a fire emergency. However, finding time to learn about fire risk management and apply that learning safely can be a tall order. Although you remain liable and cannot delegate responsibility, you can reasonably delegate some tasks to other people under the RRFSO so long as they are properly competent. To understand what this means, see *Chapter 7*.

If compliance is likely to be challenging or you are uncertain about the fire risks, you are strongly advised to seek help along the way. Under article 18 you *must* seek assistance to implement the 'preventive and protective measures' that you decide are necessary as a result of your risk assessment. Your insurer and the enforcing body can help you with your legal responsibilities and liabilities, and offer solid practical advice. Fire authorities are legally obliged to give advice to you (if you ask for it), and employ hugely knowledgeable fire safety officers for that purpose. (This is covered under the Fire and Rescue Services Act[10] and is limited to how to prevent and contain fires and how to provide a means of escape.)

Fire risk assessors and fire consultants can help with the risk assessment, prevention and protection strategies and means of escape. In certain circumstances, making use of third-party certified tradespeople or accredited testing facilities is critical.

Specifying third-party certified products, such as fire doorsets, is also a time-saving way of ensuring the construction products you purchase are compliant with fire safety requirements.

Relationship with the Building Regulations

The general level of fire safety for the structure and fabric of new buildings required by the RRFSO is met provided it satisfies the requirements of the most recent Building Regulations in England and Wales. (The same is true for equivalent legislation and technical standards in Scotland and Northern Ireland.) Of course, as soon as a new building is occupied, the fire risks change. You will still need to carry out a risk assessment and implement further measures – some of them perhaps including further building work – to comply with the RRFSO.

The Building Regulations refer to the RRFSO and efforts have been made to align the two. Of special interest is Regulation 38 of the Building Regulations, which requires that a comprehensive package of fire safety information is handed to the responsible person for new or extended premises, or where the premises have undergone a material change of use. This is specifically aimed at helping you to carry out a fire risk assessment. If you are taking possession of premises that have undergone building work that is subject to the Building Regulations, be sure to ask for this information – it will save you time and money.

However, if the structure or fabric is subsequently altered, added to, penetrated in any way, or even just decorated, the inbuilt fire protection that was incorporated within the structure of the building to satisfy the Building Regulations may be compromised and you must review it under the RRFSO.

Regardless of how old they are and which Building Regulations they satisfy, the structure and fabric of older buildings almost certainly will not meet the level of fire safety required by the RRFSO. Therefore you will need to consider the fabric of the building, understand the likely standards and codes it was built to and consider whether this is adequate for your needs. You are likely to need to commission expert third-party help from, for example, fire consultants.

It is worth remembering that certain buildings are from exempt Building Regulations. These buildings may nonetheless be captured by the RRFSO and so you must pay particular attention to whether their structure and fabric provide adequate fire protection. Restrictions on what can be done to a building – for example, if it is 'listed' in the List of Buildings of Special Architectural or Historic Interest – can make it extremely difficult and complex to comply with the RRFSO.

In essence, the RRFSO does not require all buildings to be brought up to current standards. It recognises that some work may be necessary but only in a way that is proportional to the building, its occupants and undertakings – in other words, achieving what is 'reasonably practicable'.

2 Duties, reach and enforcement

Duties and duty-holders

The definition of responsible person – you – in the RRFSO is broad and not always clear. The RRFSO says that responsible person is:

a) *in relation to a workplace, the employer, if the workplace is to any extent under his control;*

b) *in relation to any premises not falling within paragraph a)*

    (i) *the person who has control of the premises (as occupier or otherwise) in connection with the carrying on by him of a trade, business or other undertaking (for profit or not); or*

    (ii) *the owner, where the person in control of the premises does not have control in connection with the carrying on by that person of a trade, business or other undertaking.*

It may seem that the employer's responsibility for compliance depends on the extent of their control over the premises, but in practice this appears to be a red herring. A Guidance Note[11] from the Chief Fire Officers Association published in 2012 in the light of practical experience of enforcing the RRFSO says:

> *It is difficult to envisage an example whereby an employer does not have some form of control over the workplace. The very fact that a person decides to own a business or organisation which employs someone gives them a degree of control and therefore responsibility. Even if the employer has never visited the site and has put in place managers and administrators, he is still the responsible person because he has, to some extent, control over the people that work on the premises.*

If the employer is a corporate body, responsibility is jointly and severally held by the senior managers. (In these instances, the company secretary is usually the target for communication from the enforcing body.)

If there are situations where the employer of persons who work in premises do not have control of the workplace 'to any extent', the next in line would be the person who has control of the premises as occupier or otherwise or, failing that, the owner (see *Figure 2*).

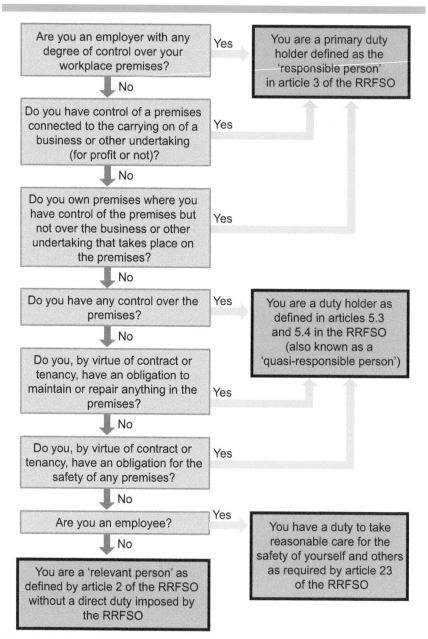

Figure 2: Guide to determining responsibilities under the RRFSO
Owing to the 'catch all' nature of the RRFSO, there will be situations that this chart does not address

Of course, employers are more likely to rent than own premises, often in buildings occupied by other undertakings. In these cases, identifying the responsible person for particular aspects of the premises is slightly harder. Within the same building there can be several different responsible persons for different aspects of that building.

Generally, the employer (the owner of the business) probably has most control and, in any case, is responsible for the safety of his or her employees, although the landlord will share some responsibility. For example, the landlord's tenancy agreement might stipulate that he retains control of the fire detection and alarm system, in which case responsibility for testing and maintaining it in good working order is his. In communal spaces such as entrance lobbies, there can potentially be many more responsible persons.

Where there are these overlaps, responsible persons from different undertakings must cooperate by communicating and coordinating their respective general fire precautions. For example, if there is a risk of an explosive atmosphere in shared premises, the person responsible for the entire premises would coordinate measures to protect relevant persons from that risk.

Occasionally, there is no employer or premises are not workplaces, such as village halls, scout huts and unoccupied premises and the like. Parts b(i) and b(ii) of article 3 deal with these situations. Nonetheless, there will still be one or more responsible persons, identified because they have some control over the premises.

Quasi-responsible persons

Article 5, which defines responsible persons' duties, says that responsibility does sometimes extend to others. The Chief Fire Officers Association calls these people 'quasi-responsible' (they are also known as '5.3/5.4 persons'). Requirements imposed on them are *in addition to* and not instead of those imposed on defined responsible persons. It includes those 'having control over premises and with contracts or tenancy agreements in relation to the safety of premises, maintenance or repair of anything in or on the premises. In both cases, responsibility extends only so far as the person has control or so far as his obligation extends'.[11]

Your duty

The duty under article 5 of the RRFSO is to 'take or observe' general fire precautions as set out in articles 8 to 22. You must take such general fire precautions as will ensure, 'so far as is reasonably practicable', the safety of your employees (or those of your employer) in the event of fire. A test of what is 'reasonably practicable' would be determined in a court of law and would be expected to consider whether the measure is grossly disproportionate to the risk.

Your duty to people who are not your employees is slightly different: you must take such general fire precautions 'as may reasonably be required in the circumstances of the case to ensure the premises are safe' (article 8(b)).

Duties of employees

Employees are not absolved from responsibility for fire safety under the RRFSO, although it is limited to matters within their personal control (article 23). They must look after themselves and other relevant persons affected by their acts. They must help the employer to carry out general fire precautions. They must be alert to unsafe situations and inform their employer about them. See *Chapter 5* for more about this. Where they have been properly trained by the responsible person and given sole responsibility for an aspect of the general fire precautions, they can be held liable under the RRFSO for any failure to carry out the duty where that failure resulted in injury or death to relevant persons.

Other important definitions

The RRFSO defines several other terms. The most important ones are:

Relevant persons: these are almost everyone, including responsible persons, in or near the premises who could potentially be put in danger by a fire at the premises.

Under the RRFSO, firefighters attending a fire at the premises are excluded from this group. In theory, it also excludes anyone on the premises unlawfully, although it is not always clear what this means.

If you are an employer, the relevant persons that you have the greatest duty to protect are employees. These are 'employees for the purposes of the Health and Safety at Work etc. Act'.

General fire precautions: these are encapsulated in articles 8 to 22 of the RRFSO, which lists:

a) *measures to reduce the risk of fire on the premises and the risk of the spread of fire on the premises;*
b) *measures in relation to the means of escape from the premises;*
c) *measures for securing that, at all material times, the means of escape can be safely and effectively used;*
d) *measures in relation to the means for fighting fires on the premises;*
e) *measures in relation to the means for detecting fire on the premises and giving warning in case of fire on the premises; and*
f) *measures in relation to the arrangements for action to be taken in the event of fire on the premises, including:*
   (i) measures relating to the instruction and training of employees; and
   (ii) measures to mitigate the effects of the fire.

The measures specifically exclude any special, technical and organisational measures:

- designed to prevent or reduce the likelihood of fire arising from 'work processes', such as the use of plant or machinery or the use or storage of any dangerous substance; or
- required to comply with the Health and Safety at Work etc Act 1974(a).

Preventive and protective measures: these are measures that are part of the general fire precautions that you identify in a risk assessment as the way to comply with the RRFSO.

Prescribed information: this is information that must be recorded, and comprises the significant findings of the risk assessment (including the measures taken or to be taken, such as training and maintenance, consultation and co-ordination) and any group of persons identified as being especially at risk. In practice, almost all risk assessments have at least some significant findings.

Dangerous substance: any substance or mixture of substances whose chemical or physical properties and presence on premises mean that it creates a risk.

Hazard: the potential of dangerous substances to give rise to fire that affects the safety of relevant persons. It is an important concept in the risk assessment.

Risk: in the context of the RRFSO, the only relevant risks are those threatening the safety of relevant persons from fire. Clearly, there are many other risks, especially to business continuity, that it might be wise to consider at the same time.

Where does the RRFSO apply?

The RRFSO applies to almost all premises. These are most often workplaces but can be any installation on land or water, tent, moveable structure, vehicle, vessel, aircraft or hovercraft.

A workplace is defined as any premises or parts of premises used 'for the purposes of the employer's undertaking'. It includes all the spaces within the workplace premises, including lobbies, corridors and staircases as well as infrequently visited spaces such as lofts, plant rooms, outbuildings, storage spaces, and so on.

There are several kinds of premises specifically excluded from the reach of the RRFSO under article 6. The most important are domestic premises. Note, though, that communal areas in blocks of flats, for example, are addressed by the RRFSO.

How is the RRFSO enforced?

In most cases, the fire and rescue authority local to the premises is the 'enforcing body' under the RRFSO. The more likely exceptions include:

- construction sites, in which case the enforcing body is the Health and Safety Executive
- most premises used by the Armed Forces, in which case it is the fire service maintained by the Secretary of State for Defence
- most sports grounds, in which case it is the relevant local authority
- premises owned or occupied by the Crown, in which case it is a fire inspector or any person authorised by the Secretary of State.

Enforcing bodies can appoint inspectors to help them in their role, and indeed, with due process, can arrange for their duties to be carried out by either the Health and Safety Executive or the Office of Rail Regulation (in rail transport situations).

Powers of inspectors

Inspectors have the power to enter premises and inspect them in whole or part, but not by force and only after producing evidence of their authority. They are only permitted to check that the requirements of the RRFSO are being complied with. They have the power to see relevant records and take copies of them. Note that employees cannot reasonably refuse requests for help from inspectors if they are able to oblige them.

Inspectors can take things away to test their fire resistance or flammability. Inspectors can cause things to be dismantled and taken for testing if they suspect them to have the potential to endanger the safety of relevant persons. In the pursuit of safety or testing and only if it can't be avoided, they are allowed damage or destroy suspect articles or substances. However, it must be in the presence of someone with responsibilities for the premises and inspectors must first have confirmed that the fire safety precautions already in place are likely to be inadequate.

Powers of enforcing bodies

Enforcing bodies can issue three kinds of notice depending on the situation (*Table 1*). These are alterations notices, enforcement notices, and prohibition notices, and must be served on responsible persons. If it happens to you but you wish to contest the notice, you may appeal it within 21 days of receipt.

Failures to comply with requirements of the RRFSO or notices issued under it are offences punishable by fines and/or imprisonment. It is an acceptable defence for those charged with an offence to claim that they took all reasonable precautions to avoid the offence and were duly diligent in carrying out and maintaining them. However, they must prove that to have done more was not 'practicable or reasonably practicable' (article 34).

In England during 2012-2013, there were 2,800 enforcement notices, 485 prohibition notices and 58 prosecutions were undertaken.

Delegating responsibility

It is accepted that other persons may record the prescribed information at your request and on your behalf, but you retain full liability.[12] Also, if you rely on a risk assessment carried out on your behalf by a person who is competent to do so, it will not relieve you from criminal liability.

Table 1: Notices issued by enforcing bodies

Type of notice	When is one issued?	Why?	How must the responsible person respond?
Alterations	When the enforcing body prohibits you from making any alterations to the premises, or the processes carried out in them, that increase the risk without consulting the enforcing body first	Because the enforcing body thinks there is a serious risk to relevant persons from features, processes, or hazards at the premises that could easily become worse if certain specified changes are made	Before making changes to the premises or the activities in them that increase the risk, the responsible person must revise its risk assessment He or she must send a copy of the revised risk assessment to the enforcing body along with details of any changes to the general fire precautions. If you appeal the notice it is suspended until the appeal is disposed of
Enforcement	When the enforcing body requires you to make changes to your general fire precautions within a certain timescale following an inspection and after consulting other bodies as necessary	Because the enforcing body thinks the premises do not comply with the RRFSO	The responsible person must make the changes required of them by the deadline. If you appeal the notice it is suspended until the appeal is disposed of
Prohibition	When the enforcing body either restricts or prohibits the use of part or all of the premises as a matter of extreme urgency. They do not need to consult anyone before issuing it	Because the enforcing body thinks there is a serious risk to relevant persons	The responsible person must cooperate with the enforcing body, eliminate or mitigate the risk, and comply with the terms of the notice until the enforcing body lifts the notice Appealing the notice will not remove it unless the court so directs

To be clear, enforcement action is taken against you, not the contractor who did the work. A contractor may well be liable to you in contract or tort for a negligently carried out action, such as a risk assessment, which may be a mitigating factor in your defence.

It is not good enough simply to assume that contractors are competent. You should investigate their competence by confirming their qualifications, certification and experience as far as possible and your appointment should clearly state that the work is connected to compliance with the RRFSO.

There is more about checking competence in *Chapter 7*.

SECTION 2: PUTTING IT INTO PRACTICE

3 Assessing the risks

The RRFSO's fundamental objective is to prevent fires. It outlines the following principles to guide you:

- Avoid risks.
- Evaluate risks that cannot be avoided.
- Combat risks at source.
- Adapt to technical progress.
- Replace dangerous things with safe or at least less dangerous ones.
- Develop a coherent overall prevention policy which covers technology, organisation of work and the influence of factors relating to the working environment.
- Give collective protective measures priority over individual protective measures.
- Give appropriate instructions to employees.

These principles should inform every stage of your efforts to comply with the RRFSO.

Risk assessment

To know what preventive and protective measures are needed for your particular circumstances you must carry out a fire risk assessment. For the purposes of satisfying the RRFSO, the only risks to assess are those that threaten the safety of relevant persons.

That said, you might find it extremely useful to assess other risks as part of a much broader emergency or business continuity plan. For example, you might want to investigate the effect of a fire on your profitability, bearing in mind that it is not uncommon for businesses to become insolvent following a fire.

Of course, fire is not the only risk: you might wish to explore at the same time the consequences of flooding, a prolonged heatwave, computer software crashes, and so on. It may be that your insurer will be interested in these added dimensions, particularly when it comes to protecting property, and that doing things to minimise the risks is rewarded with lower premiums. If so, ensure that the findings of your fire risk assessments and resulting 'preventive and protective measures' are kept separate to the other findings. This will help you in your duty to record, maintain and revise measures to the satisfaction of the enforcing body (article 9.6; see also *Chapter 6*). It will also help you to prove that you did everything 'practicable or reasonably practicable' if the worst should happen and you find yourself charged with an offence under the RRFSO.

Your risk assessment must be 'suitable and sufficient' (article 9.1). The enforcing authorities determine this by taking into account the nature of the building and the type of undertaking. The official guidance[12] says: 'In each case the determining factor is likely to be whether fire hazards have been reasonably identified, risk reduction and mitigation carried out and residual risk appropriate protection measures (including management arrangements) implemented or proposed'.

If your premises are small or low-risk premises, you might carry out the assessment yourself using publicly available guidance, such as DCLG's 5-step checklist for fire risk assessment.[13] Indeed, there is some merit to doing so because you are likely to understand the resultant precautions more thoroughly. However, you need to be confident that you can:

- identify the fire hazards (potential causes of fire)
- identify the people at risk
- identify the fire safety measures required to protect people
- review existing arrangements for management of fire safety
- record the significant findings, ie the 'prescribed information'
- formulate an action plan
- keep the assessment up to date.

If carrying out the assessment without third-party help, consult the DCLG's sector-specific guides listed in *Chapter 1* to understand what this means. They all use the same basic process, which is outlined in 'Fire safety risk assessment: 5-step checklist', described in *Figure 3*.

A more detailed systematic methodology for carrying out a fire risk assessment is set out in *PAS 79*.[14] Intended for people who have some knowledge

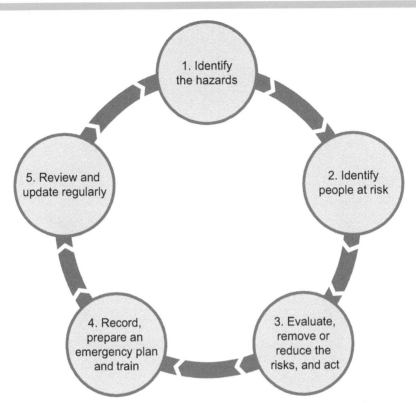

Figure 3: Assessing fire risks should be kept under continual review in a five-step process

of fire safety, it includes useful template forms and guidance on concepts, principles, and competency of assessors. It is written with the RRFSO in mind and so using it properly will help you to comply.

Clearly, the apparent simplicity of the guidance quickly disappears when the premises are large or unusual, or when the activities taking place in them are themselves complex or involve dangerous substances. Even in simple premises your particular circumstances might leave you scratching your head for lack of knowledge. In these circumstances, it is wise to call on expert help to carry out your risk assessment – see *Chapter 7* – even though you are not required to do so under the RRFSO. Note, however, that you must seek competent help 'in undertaking the preventive and protective measures' (article 18).

Young persons and other vulnerable groups

The RRFSO singles out employees who are young persons (not yet 18) as a group likely to need special consideration in the risk assessment (Part 2 of Schedule 1). It includes some guidance about what must be considered. Although not exhaustive, the checklist in *Table 2* will help you to account of the major added risks.

Table 2: Checklist: Considerations if there young persons on the premises (not comprehensive)*

Item	✓
Have you fully considered the consequences of young persons' inexperience, lack of awareness of risks and immaturity in relation to fire safety?	
Does the fitting-out and layout of the premises take young persons into account?	
Have you identified the nature, degree and duration of exposure to physical and chemical agents?	
Have you considered the form, range and use of work equipment, and the way in which it is handled?	
Is the organisation of processes and activities suited to young persons?	
Have you worked out the extent of the safety training to be provided to young persons?	
Have you assessed the risks from agents, processes and work listed in the Annex to Council Directive 94/33/EC(a) on the protection of young people at work?	
* This checklist derives from Part 2 of Schedule 1 in the RRFSO	

Clearly, there are other groups who might be especially vulnerable in a fire emergency:

- employees who are only infrequently on the premises or who work different shifts
- employees who work in isolated parts of the premises
- people who may be intoxicated, such as customers in a bar
- children (and their parents), for example, in a crèche
- people with sensory impairments that, for example, make it difficult for them to hear an alarm or see the emergency exit route
- people with restricted mobility who may, for example, need help using escape stairs
- people with mental disabilities, who may not respond safely to an alarm
- people who are ill or bed-ridden, such as hospital patients
- people who are asleep, such as hotel guests
- people who are temporarily less mobile, for example because of a broken leg
- women in the late stages of pregnancy.

If members of these groups are employees or are likely to visit the premises for any reason, you must consider the risks to them from fire and act on the findings.

Dangerous substances

The other special case singled out by the RRFSO is where you are likely to use or store dangerous substances on your premises (Part 1 of Schedule 1). No new work activity is allowed until a risk assessment has been made and appropriate measures have been properly implemented. Remember, the definition of general fire precautions excludes measures connected to work processes (article 4), although of course these are caught by health and safety legislation. Once again, although not exhaustive, the checklist in *Table 3* will help you to account of the major added risks.

Table 3: Checklist: Considerations if there are dangerous substances on the premises (not comprehensive)*

Item	✓
Have you recorded and taken account of the substances' hazardous properties?	
Have you gathered and taken account of the supplier's safety information about the substances?	
Have you considered the special, technical and organisational measures, the substances used and their possible interactions?	
Have you recorded the amount of the substance involved?	
If there is more than one dangerous substance on the premises, have you assessed the risks presented by them in combination?	
Have you worked out how to safely handle, store and transport the dangerous substances and any waste containing dangerous substances?	
Have you identified activities, such as maintenance, where there is the potential for a high level of risk?	
Will the effect of taking measures to comply with the RRFSO inadvertently increase risks?	
Have you assessed the likelihood of an explosive atmosphere occurring and how long it would persist?	
Have you identified possible ignition sources, including electrostatic discharges, and how they might start a fire?	
Have you quantified the scale of the risks?	
Have you identified places which are, or can be connected via openings to, places in which explosive atmospheres may occur?	
*This checklist derives from Part 1 of Schedule 1 in the RRFSO	

Wherever possible, avoid dangerous substances by using safer alternatives. If that is not possible, as far as possible minimise the amount you plan to use, and both minimise and control the risk to relevant persons. Arrange and vigilantly maintain safe handling, storage and transport of the dangerous substances and any dangerous waste.

Record and review

You must record your fire risk assessment (article 9.6), which must at the very least include all its significant findings and identify groups of people who are especially at risk (the prescribed information). It must be recorded as soon as practicable after it is made or reviewed. If you are an employer who employs five people or fewer then you don't *have to* record the risk assessment but it is nonetheless good practice to do so. To be clear, though, all responsible persons including the self-employed must carry out a fire risk assessment.

Figure 4: Regular audits of installation work can provide peace of mind that the work meets required standards

Do not forget to review your fire risk assessment regularly. Include it as a permanent agenda item at relevant management meetings. Be sure to consider risks that might arise because of significant changes to processes, substances stored or personnel on the premises. It is especially important to consider the effect of any building work at the premises. Identified changes to the fire risk must be recorded and followed up by appropriate action. There is more on this in *Chapter 6*.

Actions after the risk assessment

Once the risk assessment is complete, you must, with the help of one or more competent persons, work out what 'preventive and protective measures' are needed to deal with any risks that you have not managed to eliminate or avoid. There are many aspects of these measures that must not be forgotten, all covered in the next four chapters:

- A policy for preventing fires is covered in *Chapter 4*.
- A plan to deal with a fire emergency is covered in *Chapter 4*.

- Your responsibilities to communicate with relevant persons and train employees are covered in *Chapter 5*.
- The need for inspections, reviews, maintenance and records is *Chapter 6*.
- How to get competent help for assessments, audits, fire safety management, training, physical alterations or additions to your premises is explained in more detail in *Chapter 7*.

4 Implementing the fire risk assessment

Although not mentioned by name in the RRFSO, the following documents form a useful framework for actions needed:

Fire risk strategy: this is the overarching strategy you adopt to meet the RRFSO. It includes everything from management responsibilities, regular maintenance, smoking policies, training, all the way through to what you actually do when a fire occurs. Essentially it comprises everything to do with both prevention and protection.

Since it is part of the prescribed information, the fire risk strategy that you adopt on the basis of the fire risk assessment must be recorded. Doing so makes it possible to produce a document often called a Fire safety policy, which covers prevention and protection (see below).

Emergency plan: part of the fire risk strategy, the emergency plan states how to respond to a fire emergency. This includes all the things that you have done to prepare the premises for the protection of people (and perhaps property, although this is not strictly part of the RRFSO) in the event of fire. **Fire emergency procedure:** part of the emergency plan, this lists the actions to carry out when a fire occurs.

Fire safety policy – prevention

Your fire risk assessment will have allowed you to avoid or eliminate some risks, and identified how to mitigate those that are left over. Part of the mitigation process is to arrange the premises and activities within them in a way that prevents fires in the first place.

These measures vary depending on circumstances, of course, but they typically include advice to employees to store or dispose of combustible goods only in certain ways, to keep furniture, fittings and equipment in good working order (article 17 – see also *Chapter 6*), and encouragement to employees to be vigilant.

Fire safety policy – protection

After prevention, the key objective is to ensure that you can protect relevant persons in a fire. Specifically, you must establish 'appropriate procedures, including safety drills, to be followed in the event of serious and imminent danger to relevant persons' (article 15).

The policy should include an emergency plan in the event of imminent or serious danger and a way to make sure that it is implemented correctly by responsible persons, employees and other relevant persons if the need arises. This is more complex than it seems, and even for smallish premises requires a good deal of upfront planning and practice. The following are essentials:

The means to discover fire and fight it, including:

- a way to detect fire on the premises and raise the alarm (article 13)
- an appropriate automatic firefighting system, or portable firefighting equipment, such as fire extinguishers, fire blankets or, when dealing with dangerous substances, protective clothing. You must where necessary nominate competent persons – usually sufficiently trained and knowledgeable employees – to use the portable equipment (article 13)
- where there are dangerous substances involved, a way to mitigate the effects of the fire involving them (article 16)
- a system to allow people to deal with a fire involving dangerous substances – provided the risks are slight (article 16)
- a robust system for alerting the fire and rescue service (article 13)
- a system for helping the fire and rescue service to get to the fire as quickly as possible
- a regime of duly substantiated reasons to resume work in areas where there is still a 'serious and imminent danger' (article 15).

A plan for how to evacuate, including where necessary:

- clear passageways to all escape routes (article 14)
- clearly marked and lighted escapes routes and exits (article 14)
- emergency doors that open easily and in the direction of escape (article 14)
- a designated 'place of safety' or assembly point (article 14)
- a way to evacuate groups of people identified as especially vulnerable, particularly those in danger areas or who work with dangerous substances
- a way of ensuring that all relevant people have evacuated, with special emphases on young and some disabled people (article 14)
- a way to keep people from returning until the danger has passed.

Good management of the emergency plan, including:

- regular fire drills and information sharing to familiarise employees with the plan and inform them about specific hazards from dangerous substances (article 19)
- timely training for new employees (article 21)
- a programme of training and refresher courses for employees to become and remain competent to carry out specific roles (usually fire wardens) during a fire emergency (articles 15, 18 and 21)
- a system to ensure that only competent, trained people are allowed in areas of the premises known to be hazardous, and that people so exposed are adequately protected from the hazards (article 15)
- a system to ensure that the relevant accident and emergency services have the most up-to-date information about what dangerous substances are kept at the premises (article 16)
- a system of senior management control during the emergency to, for example, rule out false alarms, coordinate dialogue with the fire and rescue service when the premises are not occupied, and keep relevant persons informed, especially employees.

Fire wardens

The RRFSO obliges you to use competent people to help you to undertake the preventive and protective measures (article 18). This almost certainly means appointing members of staff to be fire wardens. Unless there is training expertise in-house, you must arrange for them to attend outside courses to become competent and thereafter to remain competent year after year for as long as you are relying on them to preserve your general fire precautions – see *Chapter 7*.

Without putting themselves in danger, fire wardens will help you to ensure an effective emergency fire evacuation in many ways, including:

- issuing verbal instructions
- assisting identified vulnerable people
- ensuring that people who cannot use stairs reach fire refuges (places of temporary safety, usually on landings at the top of stairs where they can be rescued by the fire and rescue services if no other means is available)
- knowing how to use the portable firefighting equipment
- turning off critical electrical or other equipment identified in the risk assessment

- checking that all parts of floors, including toilets, are evacuated
- directing people to the fire escape route and keeping them away from lifts
- closing doors
- reporting to or carrying out roll calls at the place of safety
- helping to prevent people from returning to the evacuated premises until it is safe to do so.

Fire wardens also have a day-to-day preventive duty to keep an eye on general fire safety, which, owing to their training, is slightly more prominent than the duty of ordinary employees – see *Chapter 5*. For example, they should help to ensure that:

- combustible materials (such as paper or packaging) are stored or disposed of safely
- the means of escape are not obstructed
- fire doors are not obviously damaged or propped open
- extinguishers are not missing or obviously damaged.

Evacuation strategies

There are four basic evacuation procedures. Which you adopt will depend on your premises, the activities carried out in them, the people present, and the precise functioning of the fire detection and alarm equipment installed:

- **Single-stage evacuations:** these are the most basic and probably the most common. Very simply, if the alarm sounds, everyone evacuates according to the plan.
- **Two-stage evacuations:** this procedure acknowledges the very real potential for false or unwanted alarms, giving responsible persons some time to investigate whether the alarm is worth an evacuation or not. Sometimes automatic fire detectors malfunction; at others, albeit they are functioning correctly, the trigger event does not merit a full alarm – such as when someone burns their toast, or when a potentially dangerous fire is extinguished early and safely. The procedure tends to build in safety-first features to avert any complacency, such as a presumption to evacuate if the trigger event cannot be found, or a time limit on how long responsible persons have to search the fire before the full evacuation alarm is sounded.
- **Phased evacuations:** this procedure takes advantage of the fact that modern construction regulations require the storeys in multi-storey buildings to delay the spread of fire to other floors long enough for people to evacuate and for firefighters to put it out. Generally, the procedure

requires people on the floor where the fire has started and on the floor directly above to evacuate, and keeps others on standby to evacuate.

- **Progressive horizontal evacuations:** this procedure is commonly used in hospitals or hospices where there are likely to be bed-ridden patients who are less easily evacuated. It takes advantage of and trusts in compartmentation – fire-resisting construction between different zones (for example, wards in a hospital) on the same floor in premises. The alarm is zone-specific and requires people in the affected zone to evacuate to an adjacent zone on the same floor. People in other zones are kept on standby until the risk has passed.

An alternative to evacuating is for occupants to stay put in the event of fire. This seems counterintuitive and indeed is only recommended in buildings where there is a low risk of the fire spreading outside of the compartment of origin (see the Section *Compartmentation* later in this chapter). In practice, stay-put as a strategy is used almost exclusively for blocks of flats and, even then, the blocks must at least have been constructed or converted in compliance with the Building Regulations 1991, Approved Document B or equivalent.[15]

The other aspects of the fire emergency procedure are also bespoke, and getting them right for your premises is not straightforward. There are many questions to answer, including:

- How do you make sure relevant persons know what different alarms mean?
- How do you make sure they will do the right things when the alarm is triggered?
- How do you know whether the doors, glazing, floor, ceiling or wall construction will resist a fire in a way that allows you to carry out your evacuation plan?
- How do you know whether your escape routes and exits are adequate?
- Which of the many proprietary products for detectors, alarms and other equipment are best suited to your circumstances?
- Will all the mechanical and electrical fire safety systems interoperate adequately with all their constituent and other connected hardware?

Fire detection and alarm systems

The fire detection and alarm systems installed can vary enormously. In a very small office with very few people and straightforward escape routes to places of safety, it may be reasonable to rely on occupants to detect a fire and for them to shout or ring a bell to raise the alarm. In most circumstances, though, it is wise to invest in a properly designed system that meets relevant performance standards. There are of course many different proprietary products, some linked to sophisticated wider building management systems, and although they might meet relevant performance standards, they must also work together where different elements make up the complete system.

There are two main types of installation:

● conventional ones that are either on or off
● addressable ones that feature a control dashboard allowing one to address each detector individually.

The addressable installations have numerous technical advantages but the main one is that it makes it easier to locate the fire or discover false alarms.

Detectors
The range of detectors includes:

● heat detectors
● smoke detectors
● asphyxiating smoke detectors
● carbon monoxide detectors
● flame detectors.

They all have their advantages and disadvantages making them more or less suitable for different situations. Specialist advice should be sought in order to ensure your system meets the requirements of your strategy.

Alarms
There is a wide range of alarms available, most audible with either loud continuous or intermittent electronic tones, or pre-recorded verbal messages. Some systems allow live instructions to be given over the top of alarm signals. There are also systems for people with impaired hearing which consist of bright warning beacons.

Firefighting
Fixed automatic firefighting installations
Sometimes it is cost-effective and commensurate with the identified risk to install automatic firefighting systems. This is often when there are

high-value or business-critical property or systems to protect, risks that fall outside of the scope of the RRFSO. However, they are used to meet RRFSO risks, especially to protect vulnerable people or to compensate for a building's construction – particularly buildings built to older building regulations. They are a potentially critical option for you and are worth considering in undertaking your preventive and protective measures.

Very broadly, there are four kinds of installation:

- automatic water sprinklers
- water mist systems
- gaseous fire suppression systems
- powder or chemical foam systems.

These are extensive installations requiring several failsafe features, and require expert help in their design, commissioning and maintenance.

Hose reels

Used and installed less frequently these days, these systems comprise risers to carry water to hoses stored in strategic locations – usually on every floor of the premises. They are activated with valves that let the water into the hose. Water is controlled through the hose nozzle, which can usually be either on or off and sometimes feature other settings to distribute water in different ways.

Portable fire extinguishers

There are many sizes and types of fire extinguisher, variously suited to different kinds of fire. None lasts longer than a few seconds after activation and so are only really useful for small fires. Some contain extinguishants that are hazardous to humans. It is absolutely critical that only the right kind of extinguisher is used for some kinds of fire, and therefore training in this area is critical.

There are five classes of extinguisher described in British Standards. They are all formally colour-coded:

- Water (red): used on fires involving solid organic materials such as paper or timber
- Foam (cream): used on fires involving liquids or liquefiable solids, such as petrol, paraffin or alcohol
- Powder (blue): used on fires involving gases, such as propane or butane

- Carbon dioxide (black): used on fires involving metals, such as magnesium, titanium and aluminium
- Wet chemical (yellow): used on fires involving vegetable or animal oils and fats as found in cooking appliances.

There is a range of other portable firefighting equipment suited to specific situations, such as fire blankets and, where dangerous substances demand it, protective clothing.

Passive fire protection

Compartmentation

Compartmentation is a technique of building fire resistance into the fabric of the walls, partitions, floors and ceilings to delay the spread of fire and smoke. The resistance should last long enough to minimise the risk to occupants, some of whom, for example fire wardens, may have to remain in the building while evacuation proceeds. It should also reduce the risk to fire fighters and relevant persons in the vicinity of the building. It is part of what is known as passive fire protection.

Containing fires in this way has obvious benefits in that it limits the risk to people, especially where the evacuation strategy depends on it – such as in hospitals or tall buildings. It safeguards escape routes and helps firefighting operations. It is also extremely important from the point of view of protecting property and limiting disruption to businesses or other undertakings. Property can be irretrievably lost by the action of the fire and smoke, and severely damaged by the water (or other extinguishants) used in firefighting. Limiting the area affected through compartmentation can be the difference between business survival and going bust.

Compartmentation and the Building Regulations

Your premises, especially if they were built recently, should already be adequately compartmented because the Building Regulations require it – see *Chapter 1*. However, a risk assessment under the RRFSO might indicate that further compartmentation is needed, for example, to separate business-specific zones of high risk on the same floor, or separate sources of ignition from combustible materials. This is especially true if you've taken possession of a shell and core, or are planning a major refit, refurbishment or alteration. In these instances, your architect or fire engineer will be able to help you meet current Building Regulations, tailored to your particular needs.

Compartmentation and how to know what is fire-resistant

Pre-existing, fire-resistant construction is hard to detect because it is usually finished in a way that is indistinguishable from ordinary construction. Fortunately, Regulation 38 of the current Building Regulations[16] requires that the layout of newly constructed fire compartments and their fire resistance is recorded for the benefit of future occupiers, specifically to help them to make an accurate fire risk assessment under the RRFSO. For older buildings, the information might be available because of historic requirements under the Construction (Design and Management) Regulations[17] or the now repealed Fire Services Act 2003.

You will need to survey the premises. Although the RRFSO is silent on the matter, common sense dictates that you should commission specialist consultants to do this for you – unless of course you are competent to do it yourself. The results of any such 'compartmentation audit' are a prerequisite to any fire risk assessment, and will form an important basis for decisions that affect the life safety of all relevant persons.

Other than the risk that building work carried out incorrectly, the single greatest challenge to a compartment's effectiveness is where during subsequent building work it is penetrated by doors, windows, glazing, telecommunication installations or services (pipes, wiring, ventilation ducts, and so on).

Fire doors

Doors into fire compartments are technically complex, highly specialised kinds of door that go by the deceptively simple name of 'fire door'. Their construction, furniture, installation and management are extremely important in the overall fire safety of premises. Without them, the function and performance of any compartment is compromised. Even with them, they must be carefully and vigilantly managed at all times if the compartment is going to serve its purpose. They also have to serve all the functions of a standard door – depending on the situation, security, sound insulation, aesthetic appeal, weather-proofing, and so on.

Fire doors can only delay the spread of fire and smoke if they are closed at the time of the fire. As they respond to heat, intumescent seals around the edges of doors or, if made of steel, the doors themselves, expand to block any gaps. This stalls the fire and the spread of hot smoke. It is just as important to block cold smoke, which does not set off intumescent seals or cause steel

41

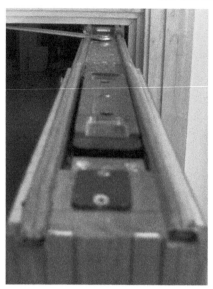

Figure 5: Incompatible security hardware can have a detrimental effect on a fire door

Figure 6: Example of a fire door that has had its hardware changed but the resulting void not made good

to expand. Its spread can be halted by fitting a separate brush or blade seal to the frame rebate or as part of the intumescent seal.

However, this critical sealing action is pointless if any part of the entire doorset is wrong. The face of the door, its core, glazing and door frame must be fire-resisting to the minimum standard. It must also have been demonstrated by test or competent third-party assessment to provide the required level of fire resistance as a complete doorset. Equally, if incompatible or unapproved door furniture penetrates through the thickness of the door or compromises the action of the seal, it could also fail. Generally speaking, it is unwise to specify anything other than unmodified, fully tested, third-party certified complete doorsets as fire doors, and have them installed by properly qualified people. There is more on this in *Chapter 7*.

Fire doors are often misunderstood. Occupants do not always understand the role they play and the impact that misuse can have on their fire resistance. You must make sure that everyone on the premises understands their importance. Most are designed to be kept shut except when in use. Propping them open for extra ventilation or to make it easier to move heavy objects through them, for example, is unacceptable. In all cases, the fact that they are fire doors must be indicated with a sign – see more below.

There are various automatic door closing systems available that, because they are linked to the automatic fire detection system and activate in the event of fire, can allow you legitimately to hold a fire door open.

Apart from being heavy, fire doors can be difficult to distinguish from normal doors. It is not unheard of for existing doors that appear to be appropriately rated fire doors to turn out not to be – sometimes after it is too late. If in doubt, seek competent specialist help.

For more information, refer to:

- Door and Hardware Federation & Guild of Architectural Ironmongers, *Code of Practice: Hardware for Fire and Escape Doors* (2012)[18]
- *BS 8214:2008 Code of practice for fire door assemblies*, BSI.
- Architectural And Specialist Door Manufacturers Association (ASDMA). *Guidance on fire door installation.*[19]

Glazing

Glazing is a common element of construction in all premises and is likely to be found on escape routes and therefore deserves special consideration. Glass needs to be considered for fire and perhaps insulation performance unless there are other mitigating solutions, such as sprinklers.

Fire glass is of two types – insulating and non-insulating.

There are limitations on the permitted use of non-insulating glass on escape routes and within walls and fire doors (see Table A4 in Approved Document B, Volume 2). It may be necessary to consider key circulation spaces, refugee points and primary means of escape as part of the risk assessment to determine whether the existing glass installation and type is suitable. If the glass is not wired or marked it will be very difficult (if not impossible) to determine whether the glass type carries any fire resistance, especially in the absence of any building information.

The performance of fire resisting glass relies on the installation method and it is therefore strongly recommended that specialist glaziers are used when replacing fire-rated glazing installations.

Take great care in how glazing is specified and beware mixing different types together for the same fire protection – they all have significantly different fire resistances and other characteristics, and must work with their frames. Once again, seeking competent specialist advice is likely to be a wise course of action.

Lighting

Unless the risk assessment finds that it is not needed, you must install emergency back-up lighting of 'adequate intensity' to light emergency routes and exits in case the normal lighting fails (article 14.2h). Possible reasonable alternatives could be to rely on battery-powered torches, or borrowed lighting from a different but dependable source, such as street lighting.

The risk assessment might also reveal that you should install emergency lighting to maintain safe working conditions for relevant persons if there are hazardous activities regularly under way in the premises. In some limited circumstances, there may also be a call for stand-by lighting to allow normal activities to carry on even though the normal lighting has failed or may involve full lighting systems with independent power sources.

Emergency lighting is once again a specialist area. Where to install it, how to protect it so that it works when normal lighting fails, how it is automatically activated, how it is powered, and how to maintain it, for example, are important questions that you will probably need answered by competent suppliers.

Signage

The RRFSO requires you where necessary to indicate non-automatic fire-fighting equipment (article 13.1b) and emergency routes and exits (article 14.2g) with signs. The extent and quantity of this signage depends on the findings of your risk assessment. Where they are installed is a matter of careful consideration. They should be unambiguous and easily visible given their context. For example, a sign indicating the way should always be within sight and legible from the farthest point along escape routes.

The design of these and other signs is set out in British Standards. Other useful signs include the 'Fire door keep shut' and the more wordy 'What to do in the event of fire' notice setting out the emergency plan.

The HSE publication *Safety signs and signals: guidance on regulations*[20] offers advice on fire safety signs.

These signs all fall into five categories:

- Prohibitory – a red circle around a pictogram with red line through it
- Warning – a black triangle on a yellow background showing a pictogram of the relevant hazard
- Mandatory – white writing on either a blue circle (applies at all times) or blue rectangle (applies during a fire emergency)
- Safe condition – white pictogram, sometimes with explanatory text, on a green background used, for example, on escape routes
- Firefighting – white pictograms or text on a red background, used to show, for example, extinguishers or manual fire alarm call points.

Escape routes

You must ensure that your premises have an adequate means – corridors, lobbies, stairways (but almost never lifts), exits and ultimate places of safety – for people to escape in a fire emergency. The Building Regulations control many aspects of the design of these escape routes, such as their width, quantity, travel distances and fire-resistance. Under the RRFSO, therefore, your responsibility usually only extends to securing that, at all material times, the means of escape can be safely and effectively used (article 4).

As critical paths to safety, escape routes require special management attention. The factors to consider are:

- **Maintaining fire resistance:** this is about ensuring that their compartmented construction has not been compromised and that fire doors or glazing remain fit for purpose. It includes ensuring that wall linings and finishes are appropriate and in good repair. For example, otherwise appropriate wallpaper will become a hazard if it peels, just as some paint finishes will if allowed to flake.
- **Good housekeeping:** escape routes must be easy to find and clearly marked, and kept free from obstructions, especially if they are combustible. Fire doors must be kept closed. Security concerns about theft or unauthorised entry must not override the ability for exit doors to be easily opened in a fire emergency. Floor finishes must be free of trip, slip or other kinds of hazards. Combustible posters, notices, or decoration should not be attached to walls.
- **Vulnerable groups:** your fire risk assessment will have highlighted especially vulnerable individuals or groups who need special consideration, and planned for how they should escape in a fire emergency. These

escape systems and associated equipment, if any, must be maintained in good working order. For example, fire refuges must be kept clear and any communication equipment in them must remain functional.

- **Fixed active systems:** smoke detectors and emergency lighting have a special role to play in the safe escape of relevant persons from premises along escape routes. They must be maintained in good working order at all times.

Inevitably, understanding the risks and instituting appropriate fire safety measures is difficult and almost certainly will need competent, preferably third-party certified, help.

5 Looking after employees and other relevant persons

Your duty under the RRFSO (articles 8 and 34) is to do everything that is practicable or reasonably practicable to protect relevant persons, particularly employees, from fire. An important factor in the success in doing so derives from the instruction and training you arrange for employees – on the assumption that you are or your undertaking is an employer.

This is critical: if you do not give them the information or train them well enough (articles 19 and 21), and practice the training in drills, they will not know what to do in a fire emergency, potentially a catastrophic situation. For example, they need to know:

- what risks they face
- how to raise the alarm
- when to tackle a fire themselves
- what the alarm sounds mean
- how to evacuate
- where to go when they do evacuate
- what actions to perform as they leave
- how to help vulnerable colleagues, visitors to the premises and other relevant persons.

More than that, without information or training relevant persons can't be expected to help you to maintain the general fire precautions on a day-to-day basis, a failing that will increase the risk and consequences of fire significantly. For example, without information, they will not know the heightened fire risks from:

- fire doors that are kept propped open
- breaches of the no-smoking policy
- untidy combustible materials stored in the wrong places
- escape routes blocked with clutter
- the ignition potential of, for example, heaters, unsafe wiring, or lighting
- damaged or obviously defective fire extinguishers, emergency lighting, or signs
- breaches of security that threaten arson.

Of the groups that make up relevant persons, only responsible and quasi-responsible persons and employees have specific duties under the RRFSO. Other relevant persons on the premises – visitors, patients, residents, shoppers, audiences, football fans, business partners, and so on – are effectively in their hands in the event of fire.

Employee's duties under the RRFSO

Article 23 requires every employee while at work to take 'reasonable care' of his or her own safety and that 'of other relevant persons who may be affected by his [or her] acts or omissions at work'.

What is reasonable in this instance is not defined but is presumably closely connected to the amount of information you give. Employees that receive timely, comprehensive, well-delivered instruction or training backed up with regular refresher courses and drills, will be better able to take care of themselves and help other relevant persons.

As the employer or a representative of your employer, it is up to you to determine what the needs of employees are on the basis of the fire risk assessment and the emergency plan. It is not a valid defence to deny employees instruction and training commensurate with the risk assessment on the basis of excessive cost. Neither is it possible to levy any such costs on any employee (article 40) or to conduct the training outside of normal working hours (article 21.2e).

Employees are also required to cooperate with you to allow you to carry out your duties, provided they have been adequately trained and instructed. Employees must inform you (or the employer or anyone else in a position of responsibility for fire safety) of any situation that they would reasonably consider was 'a serious and immediate danger to safety' or 'a shortcoming in the employer's protection arrangements for safety'. The duty to point out shortcomings only applies in so far as it either affects the employee's own safety or arises in connection with that employee's own activities at work, and has not previously been reported by other employees.

Employer's duties to inform

Only if your undertaking is an employer, the information you give to employees under the RRFSO must be 'comprehensible and relevant'. This should take account of the employees' ages, any language barriers and disabilities. Giving information is regarded as separate to training, for which there are separate duties.

Information to employees

At the very least, you must (under article 19) inform employees about:

- the risks to them identified in the risk assessment
- the preventive and protective measures
- the procedures and the measures to follow in the event that they are in serious and imminent danger
- who you have nominated for special roles to help with firefighting and fire detection, or who you have appointed to be, for example, fire wardens
- any additional risks you have learnt of from responsible persons of undertakings that share parts of the premises (under the duty to cooperate and coordinate in article 22).

If there are dangerous substances present, you must also tell employees what the substances are and their associated risks. You must let them see relevant safety data concerning the substances, including the legislated rules for using them.

If your undertaking employs children, you must explain to their parents (or person with parental responsibility):

- what risks their child will face, including those from other undertakings where premises are shared
- the preventive and protective measures.

Information to employers from outside undertakings and the self-employed

You may occasionally have visitors working at your premises that are employed by other undertakings or are self-employed. These could be, for example, building contractors or gardeners. When it comes to providing information under article 20 of the RRFSO, they are special cases.

You must ensure that the *employer* of any such employee (rather than the employee him- or herself) is informed about the preventive and protective measures that are in place and the risks to that employee. You must also tell the employer who the relevant fire wardens (and any others nominated to help people to evacuate from the premises) are. If the person is self-employed and therefore does not have an employer, you must tell the self-employed person instead.

Very occasionally you might have someone working in your undertaking (as well as on your premises) who is not your employee – someone on secondment, perhaps. You must give him or her – and not their employer – 'appropriate instructions' as well as tell them about the risks they face.

Employer's duty to provide training

It is absolutely critical that employees are trained in relation to fire safety, as set out in article 21. The training or instruction must be 'suitable and sufficient' for the individual employee to safeguard both him- or herself and other relevant persons. There is no duty to train relevant persons who are not employees.

Timing is important. On the very first day that a new employee starts work he or she must receive 'adequate safety training' more or less as the first thing that happens. Thereafter, the training should be repeated as often as you deem necessary, based on the risk assessment or any revision of it. The factors that could precipitate new or repeat training are:

- The employee is new to the workplace and unfamiliar with the risks or emergency procedures.
- The employee is transferred or given new responsibilities in the workplace.
- There is new work equipment or a change in how it is used in the workplace.
- New technology is introduced into the workplace.
- New or changed working practices are introduced into the workplace.
- The fire risk assessment finds that the employee should have a refresher after a certain amount of time.

There are other implicit duties to train under the RRFSO, all covered by your duty to take 'general fire precautions', the definition of which includes 'measures relating to the instruction and training of employees'. They include:

- The duty to nominate competent persons to implement firefighting measures implies that you will have to train them to become and thereafter stay competent (article 13).

- The training that relates to emergency action must be practised in safety drills (article 15.1a).
- The duty to nominate competent persons (fire wardens) to implement procedures, including fire safety drills, to be followed in the event of serious and imminent danger implies that you will have to train them to become and thereafter stay competent (article 15).
- The duty appropriately to instruct – apparently a lesser commitment than 'train' – any persons working in your undertaking and on your premises who are not your employees (article 20).
- If there are dangerous substances on the premises, employees must be able and competent to shut down equipment with manual overrides, which implies that they must be so trained, and should probably also undergo refresher courses as the risks demand (3 of Part 4 of Schedule 1).

Records of training

As a matter of general good practice, it makes sense to keep accurate records of the extent and timing of all employees' fire safety training. You are not compelled to keep records, however, except where you have, for example, been served with an alterations notice. Needless to say, good records will also help to show that you did everything practicable or reasonably practicable to protect relevant persons in the unfortunate event that you are charged with an offence under the RRFSO.

Fire drills

You are required under article 21.2 to give employees suitable and sufficient training on the appropriate precautions and actions to be taken by the employee 'in order to safeguard himself and other relevant persons on the premises'. This must be repeated periodically, adapted to take account of any new or changed risks, and provided in a manner appropriate to the risk identified by the risk assessment. The most important training is, of course, the fire safety drill (referred to in article 15.1).

Fire drills require all employees, not forgetting those who are often work away from the premises, to carry out the specific physical actions that ought to be followed in a fire. Not only does this reinforce 'muscle memory' – useful in the psychological disorientation that can occur in a real emergency – it also allows you the flexibility, for example, to test different fire alarm call-points, employees' familiarity with two-stage alarm signals, alternative escape routes, or how well fire wardens perform in their extra duties.

Clearly, the nature of some premises – hotels, for example – makes it awkward to carry out a fire drill. Nonetheless, you must do them. With careful planning and courteous advance warning, problems can be avoided.

Keep records of all drills together with details of any lessons learnt or difficulties encountered. These lessons must be acted on and difficulties overcome in reference to the fire risk assessment.

6 Maintaining vigilance and standards

Figure 7: A fire can quickly take hold if electrical riser cupboards are also used for storage

The passage of time erodes the effectiveness of your general fire precautions and even the relevance of your risk assessment in countless ways (*Table 4*). As the responsible person, it is extremely important not to drop your guard.

Implement robust systems to counteract any complacency, relaxation, or oversight as you would do any other important work responsibility. Techniques include:

- listing responsibilities in job descriptions
- adding permanent fire safety issues to regular meeting agendas
- setting up action checklists tailored to your premises
- building fire safety in the form of monitoring, inspections and reviews into work routines
- setting up important maintenance contracts with suitably qualified outside agencies.

If the fire safety risks are important enough and it is cost-effective, you could even directly employ a fire safety manager.

Table 4: Fire safety issues affected by the passage of time

Affecting	Examples	Effects that endanger lives
People:	People forget the information you have given them and the training they have received	They fail to respond as well in an emergency
	Success in preventing fires engenders complacency	Lowered vigilance increases the risk of fire
	People take shortcuts in or liberties with safety procedures – such as how they dispose of waste	The identified risks cease to be properly mitigated, increasing the chance of fire
	Experience and knowledge drain away as employees leave, replaced with inexperience and a lack of knowledge	There are fewer 'wise heads' to lead and show less experienced employees and other relevant persons what to do
	People sometimes have temporary mobility restrictions because of, for example, injuries or illnesses, or they are in the late stages of pregnancy	Employees who ordinarily would not need help in an emergency suddenly find that they do, with no one assigned to provide it
Processes:	Activities, processes, equipment and technology evolve	Significant changes to fire risks arise slowly, without anyone noticing and thus with no revision of the risk assessment
	Dangerous substances are stored on premises in greater quantities, or new ones are brought in	Success in business, for example, can raise consumption of dangerous substances to a point where the measures to mitigate their risks are no longer adequate
	Combustible material such as paper builds untidily in store rooms and elsewhere (poor housekeeping)	Increases fire risks, and could cause problems with means of escape especially if it has accumulated on escape routes
	Cleaning is less thorough	Build up of flammable materials, such as grease in the hoods of deep fat fryers in kitchens, increases the fire risk
	Fire doors are propped open or door closers are disabled to facilitate day to day operations such as back of house deliveries	Compromises the compartmentation, allowing smoke and fire to spread throughout the building, compromising escape routes
	Festive decorations are installed temporarily as a bit of fun	Accidentally introduces highly combustible materials or new ignition risks in normally safe environments, and increases potential for fast flash over fires
	Important signage is covered up by ongoing decoration and/or general building maintenance activities	Stops relevant persons, for example, finding emergency escape route

Table 4: Continued

Affecting	Examples	Effects that endanger lives
Equipment and construction:	Fire doors suffer damage because of poor housekeeping and/or maintenance, or are modified	Compromises the compartmentation, very significantly worsening the potential consequences of a fire
	Fire compartments are penetrated in the course of incidental property maintenance without being properly fire-stopped	Compromises the compartmentation, very significantly worsening the potential consequences of a fire
	Emergency lights fail because of poor housekeeping and/or maintenance	Makes it harder for people to find escape routes
	Extinguishers lose pressure because of poor maintenance	Renders them ineffectual for their intended use, turning a manageable small fire into a much more serious one
	Glazing is replaced with new glazing of the wrong fire rating	Compromises the compartmentation, very significantly worsening the potential consequences of a fire
	Wiring frays because of poor maintenance	Introduces new ignition hazards
	Machinery wears out because of poor maintenance	Introduces new ignition hazards
	Emergency back-up batteries run down because of poor maintenance	Compromises the functioning of the fire detection and warning and lighting systems
	Furniture upholstery tears, wallpaper peels, paint flakes because of poor maintenance	Introduces new combustible material hazards
	New equipment is introduced that is incompatible with other equipment	Compromises the functioning of the fire detection and warning systems
Management:	New risks are not identified	Managers do not notice added risks from creeping changes
	Actions in response to increased risks are not carried out	Identified problems linger and get forgotten through lapses in management control
	Emergency action plans are not updated	The risk assessment is updated but implications for emergency evacuation are missed
	Training and refresher course programmes for staff slip	People forget what they learnt previously or changes to risks invalidate some of the lessons, endangering lives

Table 4: Continued

Affecting	Examples	Effects that endanger lives
	New neighbours who share your premises move in without any reassessment of risks	Lack of coordination leads to clashes in precautions, endangering lives
	Contractors carry out work without proper arrangements for fire safety	Either their employer is not properly informed of the risks or the contractor introduces new temporary risks, endangering lives
	Instances of arson increase in your area with no resultant security action	Opportunities to strengthen security arrangements are missed
	Maintenance contracts are not reviewed	Life-critical equipment fails
	Consultants' competence is not adequately researched	Installation work falls short of safe standards

Duty to maintain

The ultimate duty to maintain general fire precautions, including the 'control, monitoring and review' of preventive and protective measures, is yours (article 5). Under article 17, you must 'ensure that the premises and any facilities, equipment and devices provided in respect of the premises' – including those that are for the protection of firefighters (article 38) – are 'subject to a suitable system of maintenance and are maintained in an efficient state, in efficient working order and in good repair'. These arrangements must be recorded unless you employ fewer than five people (and do not have a duty to do so because, for example, you have been served with an alterations notice).

There can also be a similar duty for quasi-responsible persons who have control over the premises by virtue of any contract or tenancy obliging them to maintain and repair (article 5). This duty, though, is limited to the boundaries of their obligation. A person charged with checking light bulbs in emergency lighting is not held responsible for maintaining the lighting system in its entirety.

If you are uncertain whether you have a duty to maintain, for example, parts of the premises you share with other undertakings, you must, as a matter of urgency, communicate with responsible persons at those other undertakings and 'make arrangements' with them to ensure that a suitable maintenance system is in place. The duty to cooperate is mutual (article 22).

What is maintenance?

Maintenance ensures that your general fire precautions continue to work over time, and should be proactive not reactive. The process describes a whole range of different activities. Which of these activities is undertaken varies depending on the circumstances. The hope is that when everything is checked it is found to be in perfect working order. If it is not working, however, you must remedy the situation straight away or as soon as the risks demand. Maintenance can involve:

- **Constant, day-to-day or ad hoc monitoring:** usually by responsible persons or nominated employees, with the help of other employees. For example, keeping escape routes clear of obstructions.
- **Regular inspection:** usually by responsible persons or nominated employees, with the help of other employees. For example, a weekly check of the functioning of all or a proportion of the emergency lights.
- **Periodic review:** for management processes, and usually carried out by responsible persons. For example, reviewing the risk assessment because of some new work activity.
- **Regular cleaning:** usually by employees or outside contractors. For example, to avoid the build-up of oil or fat in cooker vents.
- **Testing:** usually by responsible persons if properly competent, or by competent outside contractors. For example, a weekly sounding of the fire alarm.
- **Servicing:** for complex jobs – for example, a six-monthly service of a fixed firefighting system – usually by competent outside contractors, third-party certified if possible. If properly competent and the work isn't too complex (such as pressing 'test' on a panel), responsible persons can carry out these tasks.
- **Repairing and replacing:** usually by competent outside contractors, third-party certified if possible. For example, fixing fire doors or malfunctioning control panels for addressable fire detection and alarm systems.

In every instance it is good practice to ensure, as far as practicable, that people who maintain your fire safety systems are competent to do so. Some maintenance jobs are relatively straightforward and non-technical and can be carried out by employees such as janitors, fire wardens or receptionists. Other maintenance jobs are more about management vigilance, and can be undertaken by you. However, where you have complex technical or life-critical installations, it is wise to use outside appropriately qualified and third-party certified contractors or consultants if possible – see *Chapter 7*. *Table 5* lists examples of systems that need maintenance.

Note, though, that not all parts of the maintenance of complex systems are complex. Make a point of always asking commissioning engineers and installers to explain what aspects of maintenance are easily carried out by responsible persons (or those designated by the responsible person as competent to carry out the activity), especially if they must be carried out more regularly than a full servicing requires. This will save you money without any loss of safety.

The fire risk assessment is the key tool for keeping track of risks as they change over time. You have a duty to review it 'regularly' to keep it up to date, to record the findings and, where the risks have changed, you must amend your preventive and protective measures accordingly.

Table 5: Systems that need maintenance

Construction, system or equipment	Examples of maintenance duties	Function	Frequency	Guidance
Escape routes	· All routes must be free of obstructions · Stairs must be free of tripping or slip hazards · Some corridors and exits must not be narrowed beyond a regulated limit · Emergency escape doors must swing in direction of escape	Monitor, test in drills, report, record and, if necessary, act immediately	Constant; fire drills regularly	Must understand the design intent.
Work machinery	· Bearings must not overheat through lack of lubrication · Dust must not build up · Vents must remain clear · Driving belts must be correctly tensioned · Spillages of oil must be prevented using drip trays · Safe layout must not be compromised · Area must remain tidy	Inspect, service, report, record and, if necessary, act as risks demand	Regular and frequent	Must understand the design intent Must understand risk of fire Must understand work operation procedures
Electrical equipment	· Must not be misused · Must be free of defects · Equipment that uses heat must have adequate stands and guards and combustible material must be kept clear · Warning indicators require a response · Avoid the use of extension leads or overloading sockets · Should be turned off when not in use	Monitor, report, record and, if necessary, act as risks demand	Constant; test and inspect periodically	Must be tested and inspected periodically in compliance with BS 7671[22] Portable electrical appliances should comply with the Electricity at Work Regulations[23]

Table 5: Continued

Construction, system or equipment	Examples of maintenance duties	Function	Frequency	Guidance
Cooking equipment	• Must be kept clean • Thermostatic controls must be accurate • Extract ducts must be free of fat and oil	Monitor, report and, if necessary, act as risks demand	Constant; test periodically	Must understand the design intent Must understand risk of fire Must understand work operation procedures
Heaters	• As far as possible, must remain fixed • Furnishings, paper, timber and other combustible materials must be kept away from these • Nothing must be put on these • Portable heaters must securely guarded and prevented from falling over	Monitor and, if necessary, act as risks demand	Constant	Must understand the design intent Must understand risk of fire Must understand work operation procedures
Barriers to premises: walls, fences, roofs, etc.	• Must be kept in good repair to keep out arsonists and vandals (as well as for the usual reasons such as security, weather-proofing etc)	Inspect and, if necessary, act as risks demand	Periodically	Minor attempts to break in can presage more serious attempts
Points of entry to or exit from the premises: gates and windows	• Check that security fastenings are in good repair to keep out arsonists and vandals (as well as for the usual security reasons) • Ensure that emergency escape is not compromised when premises are occupied	Inspect and, if necessary, act as risks demand	Depends on location but probably constantly	The Fire Protection Association has good guidance on security measures and arson risk[24] Advise security staff and employees

Landscape/ gardens	• Keep clear of combustible materials • Do not allow to become overgrown in such a way as to compromise security	Monitor and, if necessary, act as risks demand	Depends on circumstances and season	The Fire Protection Association has good guidance on security measures and arson risk Advise security staff and employees
Non-automatic fire-fighting equipment	• Check not been used, tampered with or damaged • Must be in designated place • Must be accessible and visible, with operating instructions to the fore • Pressure gauge must be in range	Inspect, service, record	Monthly, with more in-depth service yearly by competent person, with any maintenance work third-party certified	BS 5306-3[25]
Compartmentation	• Structural integrity must be maintained: ensure walls, doors, glazing and shutters etc that make up the compartment are free from damage • Ensure that if penetrated to install services, for example, the penetrations are adequately fire-stopped	Monitor and, if necessary, act immediately	Regular and frequent	The Association for Fire Protection publishes useful guidance in this area[26] Use certified or at least trained personnel
Fire doors	• Ensure all parts of doorset are free of damage and not altered or modified (except by properly competent persons)	Monitor and, if necessary, act immediately	Constant	ASDMA[27] and the Door and Hardware Federation[28] (DHF) guides Use certified or at least trained personnel to carry out maintenance
All plant and services	• Ensure kept in good working order	Test, inspect, service, record and, if necessary, act as risks demand	As recommended by manufacturer or installer, commensurate with risks	Must understand work operation procedures

Table 5: Continued

Construction, system or equipment	Examples of maintenance duties	Function	Frequency	Guidance
Automatic fire alarm systems	◦ Must be kept in good working order	Test, inspect, service, record and, if necessary, act immediately	Service every six months or as recommended by commissioning engineer/ insurer; weekly tests are common	BS 5839-1[29] Several guides to BS 5839 are available, for example from BSI, Fire Protection Association and various manufacturers
Emergency escape lighting system	◦ Check for battery charge ◦ Ensure that bulbs are working at all times ◦ Service standby generators ◦ Check stocks of spare consumables such as bulbs	Test, inspect, service, record and, if necessary, act immediately	Periodically	BS EN 50172[30] Keep design layouts and wiring drawings to aid contractors and others when making references to specific units or items of equipment
Water and water mist sprinkler systems	◦ Must be kept in good working order	Test, service, record and, if necessary, act immediately	Periodically – as stipulated in standards and recommended by commissioning engineer	A certificate of conformity only remains valid while a maintenance contract is in place
Gaseous fire suppression systems and powder and chemical foam systems	◦ Must be kept in good working order ◦ Must check for changes to fire hazards, configuration of the protected volume	Test, service, record and, if necessary, act immediately	Regularly as recommended by commissioning engineer or supplier and to meet standard	Competent, third-party certified engineer required to service BS EN 15004-1[31]

Hose reels	○ Must be kept in good working order	Test, service, inspect and, if necessary, act immediately	Regularly	BS EN 671-3[32] BS 5306-1[33]
Fire door closers	○ Whether automatic or manual, they must be kept in good working order	Monitor, inspect, record and, if necessary, act immediately	At least once every six months	ASDMA and the Door and Hardware Federation (DHF) guides Use certified or at least trained personnel to carry out maintenance
Fire resistant glazing	○ Check for faults or other changes made by unqualified contractors	Inspect, record and, if necessary, act immediately	Regularly according to programme set by fire risk assessment	Glass and Glazing Federation (GGF) best practice guide[34] Use, trained personnel or certified specialist glaziers

7 Doing all that is reasonably practicable

Regardless of the RRFSO, you will want to do what is reasonably practicable to ensure the safety of people you are responsible for in the event of fire, while spending budgets wisely. The RRFSO merely makes this law.

The definition of what is reasonably practicable is open to interpretation and, in the event of prosecution under the RRFSO, you have to *prove* that you acted with due diligence. There is likely to be a range of responses that meet this requirement for any given situation with, at one end, a 'belt and braces' approach and, at the other, a 'just good enough' approach. 'Just good enough' is just that; enforcement notices and prohibition notices are not issued by the Fire and Rescue Service when the situation is just good enough. If a notice is issued it is because things are just *not* good enough.

Grey areas can be resolved by the Secretary of State as a dispute resolution.

There is a lot to consider, much of it requiring considerable baseline knowledge, experience and expertise – competence. The RRFSO recognises this and, although it limits the extent to which it explicitly requires you to call in competent persons (see *Table 6*), your duty to do everything reasonably practicable means that doing so is frequently implicit.

For example, you do not have to use a specialist to help you to carry out your fire risk assessment. However, if in doubt about your abilities or indeed the time you can devote to doing it properly, appointing a specialist is a better bet. Bear in mind that nearly every successful prosecution under the RRFSO includes not undertaking a suitable and sufficient fire risk assessment.

Sometimes, though, even if you yourself are competent, you must still seek help. Indeed, article 18 requires you, with a few exceptions, to appoint competent persons to help you to 'undertake the preventive and protective measures'. Notwithstanding the exceptions, it seems safest to rely on properly qualified and/or third-party accredited expert help, preferably with directly relevant experience of your kind of premises. If there is a competent person employed directly by the employer, you must use him or her to undertake the preventive and protective measures. If not, of course, you must use an outside consultant.

Table 6: When competent persons are needed

Function	RRFSO requires
Undertake preventive and protective measures	The responsible person 'must appoint one or more competent persons to assist him in undertaking the preventive and protective measures' (article 18)
Equip the premises with firefighting equipment, fire detectors, alarms, etc as appropriate	The responsible person must 'nominate competent persons to implement those measures and ensure that the number of such persons, their training and the equipment available to them are adequate, taking into account the size of, and the specific hazards involved in, the premises concerned' (article 13)
Procedures, including safety drills, to be followed in the event of serious and imminent danger to relevant persons	The responsible person must 'nominate a sufficient number of competent persons to implement those procedures in so far as they relate to the evacuation of relevant persons from the premises' (article 15)
Measures in respect of dangerous substances	The 'means for manual override must be possible, operated by employees competent to do so, for shutting down equipment and protective systems incorporated within automatic processes which deviate from the intended operating conditions, provided that the provision or use of such means does not compromise safety' (3 in Part for of Schedule 1)

Specific references in the RRFSO require the responsible person to use competent persons to help with their general fire precautions. Competent people are those who have sufficient training and experience or knowledge and other qualities to allow them to do the specific job. This definition is explicit except for measures in respect of dangerous substances.

You have to give competent persons the means and enough time to do their jobs. This will inevitably vary depending on the size of the premises, the risks and the distribution of those risks through the premises. Cutting corners or going for a cheap option are likely to be false economies and are really not worth the gamble. You must also brief competent persons fully about the risks – including those from dangerous substances – and all the employees at risk.

How do you know when people are competent?

People are regarded as competent when they have 'sufficient training and experience or knowledge and other qualities' for the job in question. In the context of the RRFSO, there is a vast body of knowledge, making it difficult for one person to be truly competent in all subjects. Equally, the extent of the knowledge needed depends entirely on the job. The skills, competence and experience needed to adequately check that a lightbulb is working are very different to those needed to install a computerised fire detection and alarm system linked to wider building management system.

You are likely to need help for a huge range of jobs:

Risk assessment:

- undertaking it in whole or part
- audits or inspections to work out the effectiveness (such as fire resistance) of existing structures, installations and systems in your premises
- identifying hazards
- identifying risks
- identifying vulnerable groups of people
- working out how to eliminate or avoid risks
- assessing residual risks
- appraising options holistically, including for cost-effectiveness and insurance purposes
- designing commensurate preventive and protective measures to mitigate residual risks
- agreeing a fire policy and fire emergency action plan
- consulting enforcing authorities and other responsible persons
- recording the findings in an appropriate way.

Implementation:

- carrying out building works to make new fire compartments
- installing and commissioning new passive and active fire protection measures
- training fire wardens and other competent persons
- publishing effective information about fire safety
- training all staff
- designing fire drills
- recording activity in an appropriate way.

Maintenance:

- maintaining passive and active fire protection measures
- reviewing the fire risk assessment in the light of changes

- reviewing information, training and the fire safety policy and fire emergency action plan.

External services

Unsurprisingly, there is a small but growing industry of fire safety consultants who can help, offering a wide range of services. The Association of Fire Consultants, for example, lists 13 services:

- Fire safety engineering design: advice on all types of building and structures, new and existing
- Fire risk assessment
- Fire safety audit and inspection: reviewing existing precautions and/or procedures against defined performance criteria
- Fire safety training
- Fire detection system selection, design and evaluation
- Fire suppression system selection, design and evaluation
- Passive fire protection selection, design and evaluation: protecting buildings and structures generally (but not always) using applied fire protective products and materials
- Product assessments: assessing how fire protection products perform or compare based on fire test evidence
- Means of escape design and evaluation
- Computer modelling
- Preparation of fire safety standards and documentation
- Research projects
- Fire investigation.

The consultants who perform these services are represented by trade associations and professional institutions, some of which hold registers of members who must qualify for entry. In other words, the associations attempt to control the quality of the workmanship offered by their members.

Checking competence and suitability

For complicated technical systems, the people who carry out the work should be, if possible:

- appropriately qualified
- individually assessed by a certification body accredited by the United Kingdom Accreditation Service (UKAS) – for the work you've asked them to do

- belong to a reputable institution or association where there is some barrier to entry
- have experience of premises and undertakings similar to yours.

You can confirm UKAS accreditation of certification bodies for free at www.ukas.com.

The work they carry out should be, if possible:

- certified, preferably third-party certified
- to the appropriate British Standard if it exists.

The materials and products they use or specify should be, if possible:

- tested to the appropriate British Standard
- appropriately CE-marked or otherwise certified or quality controlled
- quality assured in some way to interoperate with other products or materials.

Third-party certification: do it once, do it right

Third-party certification is the provision by an independent body of written evaluation (a certificate) that the product, service or system in question meets specific requirements or standards.

In the context of the RRFSO, the reason for getting something independently evaluated is to confirm it meets specific requirements to reduce risks to life from fire. Most commonly, these evaluations are for the calibration of equipment, testing products, inspecting equipment and certifying quality management systems.

Third-party certification is not a legal requirement and, indeed, is not available for everything. However, where available, it does evaluate quality in manufacture, installation and maintenance. For example, third-party certification of products evaluates the ongoing quality of products on the production line. Third-party certified installation or maintenance services give you confidence that the performance of life-critical products is not compromised in your premises. Incorrectly installed fire doors, for example, may not function correctly as a fire door. Long term, this certification is very likely to be more cost-effective than doing without.

Figure 8 shows typical certification processes for products, installation and maintenance.

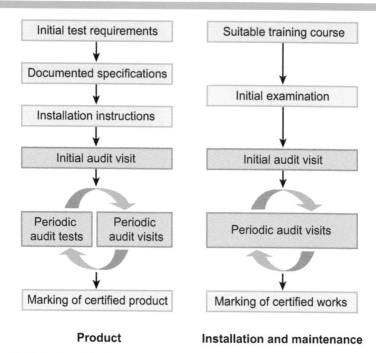

Figure 8: Typical certification processes

Accreditation – peace of mind

Accreditation is the formal recognition by an independent body, generally known as an accreditation body, that a certification body operates according to international standards. Accreditation is not compulsory, and the fact that it is not accredited does not necessarily mean that a body is not reputable, but it does provide independent confirmation of competence.

In the UK, the United Kingdom Accreditation Service (UKAS) is the recognised accreditation body.

Two routes to compliance

Getting the right products and services to meet your duties under the RRFSO is confusing and complex. There are two routes to peace of mind. One is a DIY route which for most premises requires a lot of detailed technical and up-to-date knowledge, and is thus risky. The other is the route of engaging with third-party certified product manufacturers, installers and maintainers, which, although still requiring due diligence on your part, reduces your overall risk. To illustrate the differences, see *Tables 7 to 9* using the example of replacement fire doors.

As the result of your fire risk assessment for a hotel, you discover that you must replace 10 fire doors. Quality and competence are critical issues.

If you were to start from scratch when selecting fire doors, you would need to get answers to the questions listed in *Table 7*. But when you specify

Table 7: Sourcing fire doors

Item
The following questions must be satisfied:
Test evidence: 1. Can the manufacturer provide test evidence for the door(s)? 2. Is it to the correct standard? 3. Is the manufactured product identical to the one that was tested? 4. If the test was conducted by another company, is the manufactured specification the same as tested?
Factory processes (or Factory Production Control (FPC)): 1. What processes are used to ensure that the door is consistently manufactured to the originally tested specification? 2. Do the manufacturers work to written specifications?
Ongoing performance verification: 1. What checks do the manufacturers do to verify ongoing product performance?
Even if the answers to these questions are satisfactory, you should... 1. Make sure the manufacturer has a documented factory production control process in place (such as ISO 9001) 2. Check that the manufacturer has a specific understanding of the product (such as training records) – sometimes they make products without necessarily understanding the eventual application 3. Make sure the manufacturer has in place a documented process that verifies ongoing product performance. Even minor variations in the manufacturing process can critically affect the performance of the product

Not third-party certified	**Third-party certified**
Risks · May be non-compliant · May be to the wrong standard · Manufacture process might have changed subsequent to test · Manufacturing process may not be quality assured · May not be fit for purpose · May not perform its intended role (resist the passage of fire) · Costs time and money	Benefits · Asks the questions of manufacturers on your behalf · Provides confidence that the product will be fit for purpose · Provides confidence that the product will perform · Reduces risk of product failure · Saves you time and money

third-party certified fire doors, the critical questions are answered for you. And you avoid the risks and reap the benefits summarised in *Table 7*.

Figure 9 shows when happens when testing a fire doorset. The doorset on the left has failed because it was not assembled correctly. Specifying third-party certified firedoors reduces the risk of failure by ensuring consistent manufacture and installation.

Similarly, when sourcing a contractor, specifying third-party certification will answer the questions shown in *Tables 8* and *9*, so you can enjoy the benefits of third-party certification.

Table 8: Sourcing a contractor

Item
The following questions must be answered satisfactorily:
Questions you should ask an installer to determine competence • What formal training have the contractors undertaken? • What qualifications do they have? • What installation experience have they had? • Is their work subjected to on-going monitoring and, if so, by whom?

Not third-party certified	Third-party certified
Risks • You cannot verify the answers • You cannot establish whether their experience is adequate • You have no assurance of quality • Leaves you exposed to hidden dangers • Costs you time and money	Benefits • Asks the questions of installers on your behalf • Provides confidence that the product will be installed correctly • Provides confidence that the product will perform as required • Reduces risk of product failure • Prevents hidden dangers • Saves you time and money

Whichever route you take, the general attitude is to be sceptical. Never assume that a product, service or third-party certificate will deliver what you need without checking – and recording this check. In the unlikely event that you suffer a fire, not only will this help to save lives and minimise damage, it will also prove to investigating authorities that you were duly diligent.

Test set up

After 3 minutes

After 4 minutes

After 6 minutes

After 8 minutes

After 10 minutes

After 13 minutes

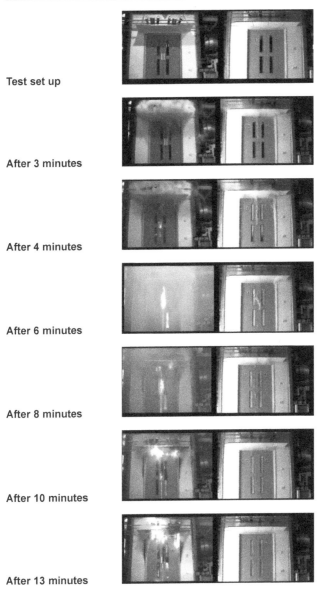

Figure 9: Fire testing of doorsets

Table 9: Sourcing a maintenance contractor

Item
The following questions must be answered satisfactorily:
Questions you should ask a maintainer to determine competence 1. What formal training have the maintainers undertaken? 2. What qualifications do they have? 3. What maintenance experience have they had? 4. Is their work subjected to on-going monitoring and if so by whom? 5. If damage is being rectified, can they demonstrate that the repair will restore the fire resistance of the product?

Not third-party certified	Third-party certified
Risks • You cannot verify the answers • You cannot establish whether their experience is adequate • You have no assurance of quality • Costs you time and money	Benefits • Asks the questions of maintainers on your behalf • Provides confidence that the product will be maintained correctly • Provides confidence that the product will continue to perform • Reduces risk of product failure • Saves you time and money

What can go wrong?

There are many things that can make a product unsuitable or a service less than competent but not all are predictable. Unfortunately, every situation is different and so there is no hard and fast list of things that go wrong that you can rely on to prove your diligence. However, the kinds of predictable glitches that you ought to look out for include:

- products being tested to out-of-date standards
- products being manufactured differently without being re-tested
- products that are certified as suitable for one use being incorrectly specified for a different use
- products that by themselves are suitable but which in combination are not
- suitable products that are subsequently modified in a way that means that they are no longer suitable
- service providers who are experienced but not adequately qualified
- service providers who are qualified and experienced but not adequately up-to-date in their knowledge
- service providers who are qualified and experienced but in different kinds of premises or for the wrong technologies
- service providers whose accreditations or qualifications have expired.

So, if relying on a product's stated suitability, check that:

- it is CE-marked[35] or otherwise third-party certified
- the test results are relevant to how you will use the product
- the test used was to current standards
- the test results are for the product you've specified
- the product was manufactured in the same way as the product used in tests.

Rules of thumb for compliance

Remember, liability for the fire safety of people in and around your premises remains yours under the RRFSO, even if it is sometimes shared with others.

- Brief the work that others carry out in your name carefully by referring to specific identified risks and the need to comply with the RRFSO.
- Make sure you keep an eye on and understand the work that they do.
- Satisfy yourself that their work deals with the fire risk identified in the risk assessment, and formally sign it off.
- Consider whether their work adds new risks, even temporarily, and act on it.
- Keep a record of their work.
- Understand the life of the product or system and what needs to be done to keep it working.
- Establish a programme of planned maintenance for all measures and, if the work cannot be carried out properly in-house, agree maintenance contracts with outside agencies to do it for you.
- Be sure to involve your insurer for advice and, potentially, improved premiums.

References

1 S.I. 2005 No. 1541. *Regulatory Reform (Fire Safety) Order 2005*, www.legislation.gov.uk/uksi/2005/1541/made

2 www.scotland.gov.uk/Topics/Justice/policies/police-fire-rescue/fire/FireLaw

3 www.nifrs.org/firesafe

4 www.gov.uk/government/collections/fire-safety-law-and-guidance-documents-for-business

5 www.lacors.gov.uk/lacors/upload/19175.pdf

6 www.local.gov.uk/c/document_library/get_file?uuid=1138bf70-2e50-400c-bf81-9a3c4dbd6575

7 www.hse.gov.uk/pubns/priced/hsg168.pdf

8 Figures derive from the UK Government's latest Fire Statistics for Great Britain – www.gov.uk

9 Figures derive from Department of Transport's latest *Reported Road Casualties in Great Britain* – www.gov.uk

10 Fire and Rescue Services Act 2004, www.legislation.gov.uk/ukpga/2004/21/introduction

11 Chief Fire Officers Association (2012), *Guidance Document: Collected Perceived Insights into and Application of the Regulatory Reform (Fire Safety) Order 2005 for the Benefit of Enforcing Authorities*, www.cfoa.org.uk/download/19059

12 Regulatory Reform (Fire Safety) Order 2005 Guidance Note No. 1: Enforcement, Department for Communities and Local Government, 2007, www.ruralurbanplanning.co.uk/guidance1enforcement2005-Enforcement.pdf

13 *Fire safety risk assessment: 5-step checklist*, Department for Communities and Local Government, www.gov.uk/government/uploads/system/uploads/attachment_data/file/14899/fsra-5-step-checklist.pdf

14 PAS 79:2012 *Fire Risk Assessment. Guidance and a recommended methodology*, BSI

15 Local Government Association (2012), *Fire safety in purpose-built blocks of flats*, Local Government Association, 2012, www.lacors.gov.uk/lacors/upload/19175.pdf

16 S.I. 2010 No. 2214: *The Building Regulations 2010*, www.legislation.gov.uk/uksi/2010/2214/regulation/38/made

17 S.I. 2007 No. 320: *The Construction (Design and Management) Regulations 2007*, www.legislation.gov.uk/uksi/2010/2214/regulation/38/made

18 www.firecode.org.uk

19 www.asdma.com/knowledge-centre

20 England and Wales Building Regulations: Approved Document B (Fire Safety), Volume 2 - Buildings other than dwellinghouses, NBS, 2013, www.planningportal.gov.uk

21 *Safety signs and signals: guidance on regulations*, Health and Safety Executive, www.hse.gov.uk

22 BS 7671: 2008+A2:2013 *Requirements for electrical installations. IET Wiring Regulations*, Seventeenth Edition, BSI

23 S.I. 1989 No. 635: *The Electricity at Work Regulations 1989*, www.legislation.gov.uk/uksi/1989/635/made

24 See, for example, *Essentials of Fire Safety Management, Second Edition*, FPA & RISC Authority, 2014

25 BS 5306-3: 2009: *Fire extinguishing installations and equipment on premises. Commissioning and maintenance of portable fire extinguishers. Code of practice*, BSI

26 www.asfp.org.uk/index.php

27 www.asdma.com/knowledge-centre

28 www.dhfonline.org.uk

29 BS 5839-1: 2002: *Fire detection and fire alarm systems for buildings. Code of practice for system design, installation, commissioning and maintenance*, BSI

30 BS EN 50172: 2004, BS 5266-8: 2004. *Emergency escape lighting systems*, BSI

31 BS EN 15004-1: 2008: *Fixed firefighting systems. Gas extinguishing systems. Design, installation and maintenance*, BSI

32 BS EN 671-3: 2009: *Fixed fire fighting systems. Hose systems: Maintenance of hose reels with semi-rigid hose and hose systems with lay-flat hose*, BSI

33 BS 5306-1: 2006: *Code of practice for fire extinguishing installations and equipment on premises. Hose reels and foam inlets*, BSI

34 www.ggf.org.uk

35 *Getting started with CE marking for construction products*, ISBN 978-1909594067, BM TRADA, 2013

Other reading

Don't take the risk: Insist on third party certification

Q-Mark fire door manufacture scheme

Q-Mark fire door installation scheme

Q-Mark fire door maintenance scheme

at www.bmtrada.com/product-certification/bm-trada-q-mark-product-schemes